LOVE WILL FIND A WAY!

RAVETTE PUBLISHING

- FITZPATRICK -

First published in 2013 by
Ravette Publishing Limited
PO Box 876, Horsham
West Sussex RH12 9GH

ISBN: 978-1-84161-367-3

STAND BY FOR THE COUNT-DOWN FRED – 10
9
8
7
6
5
4
3
2
1
THEY'RE OFF!
BATH
28

'You youngsters ought to be in bed!'
PAR
KEEP OFF THE GRASS
Taylor

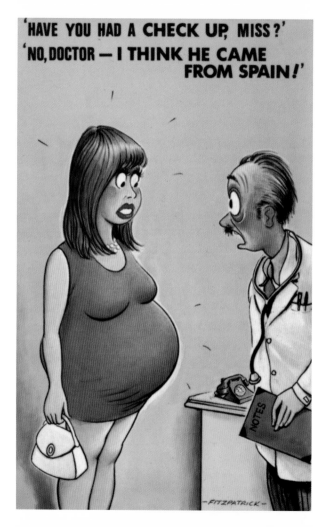

Other titles available in this series …

	ISBN	Price
Down with Drink	978-1-84161-368-0	£5.99

HOW TO ORDER:

Please send a cheque/postal order in £ sterling, made payable to 'Ravette Publishing' for the cover price of the book/s and allow the following for post & packing …

UK & BFPO	70p for the first book & 40p per book thereafter
Europe & Eire	£1.30 for the first book & 70p per book thereafter
Rest of the world	£2.20 for the first book & £1.10 per book thereafter

RAVETTE PUBLISHING LTD
PO Box 876, Horsham, West Sussex RH12 9GH
Tel: 01403 711443   Fax: 01403 711554   Email: ingrid@ravettepub.co.uk

Prices and availability are subject to change without prior notice